Gahan Wilson's Even Weirder

Forge Books by Gahan Wilson

Still Weird
Gahan Wilson's Even Weirder

Gahan Wilson's Even Weirder

A Tom Doherty Associates Book

New York

This is a work of fiction. All the characters and events portrayed in this book are either fictitious or are used fictitiously.

Some of the material in this book has appeared previously in *Playboy* and *The New Yorker*.

This book is printed on acid-free paper.

A Forge Book
Published by Tom Doherty Associates, Inc.
175 Fifth Avenue
New York, NY 10010

Forge® is a registered trademark of Tom Doherty Associates, Inc.

Design by Susan Hood

Library of Congress Cataloging-in-Publication Data

Wilson, Gahan.
[Even weirder]
Gahan Wilson's even weirder.
p. cm.
"A Tom Doherty Associates book."
ISBN 0-312-85885-X
1. Eccentrics and eccentricities—Caricatures and cartoons.
2. American wit and humor, Pictorial. I. Title.
NC1429.W5785A4 1996
741.5'973—dc20 96-23678
CIP

First Edition: November 1996
Printed in the United States of America
0 9 8 7 6 5 4 3 2 1

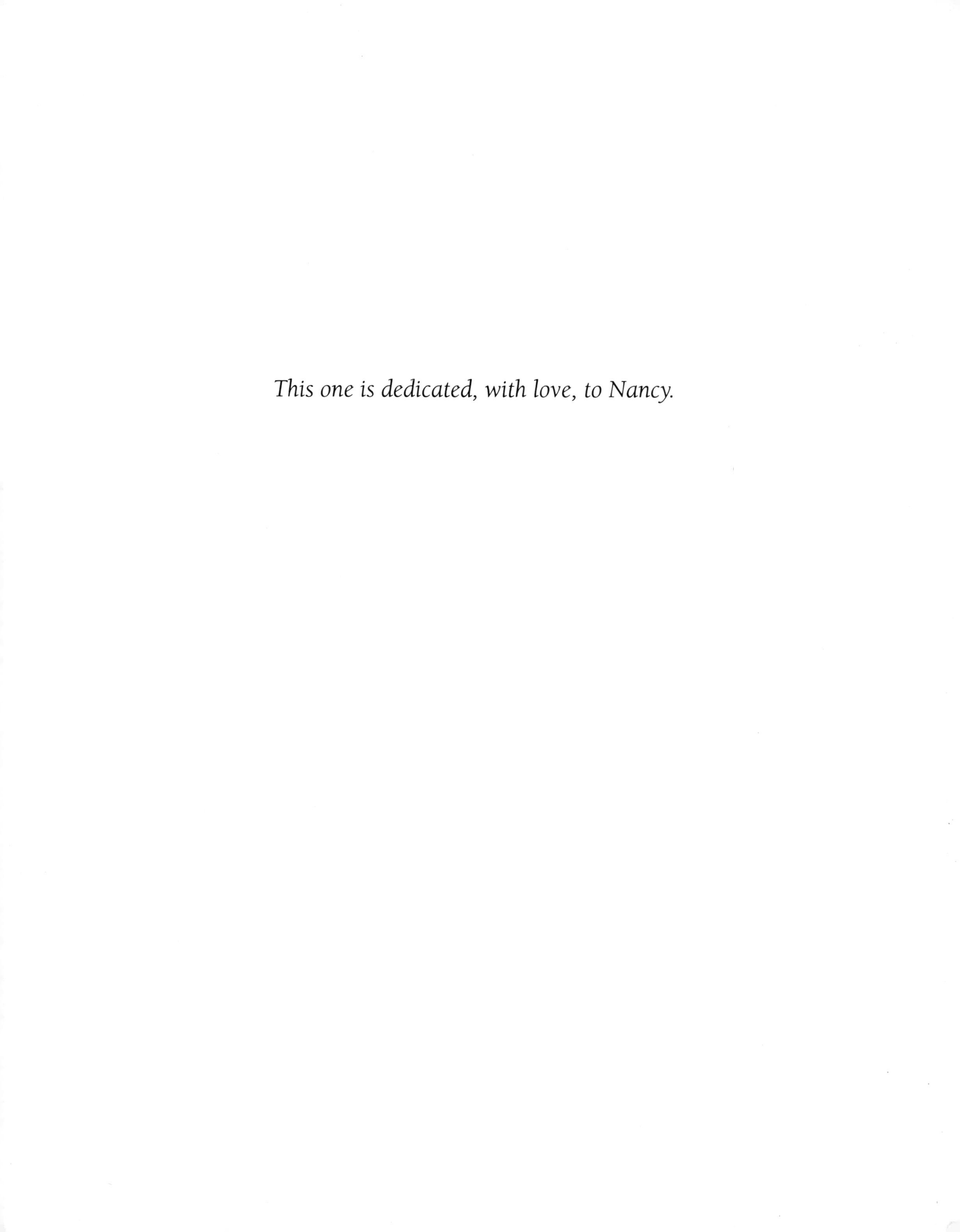

This one is dedicated, with love, to Nancy.

"WHO'S THERE?!?"

"Attorney for the prosecution will cease shaking the witness like a pit bull terrier or be in contempt of court!"

"It's a real shame when these mystery weekends go wrong!"

"I'm so glad you've called to offer me this investment opportunity because it gives me a chance to test my new telephonic death ray."

"Here he is!"

PLEASE TAKE A NUMBER
ACME

"Hold it, Fred—that's only something *pretending* to be a subway train!"

“I’m sorry—I still can’t make out what you’re trying to say.”

"I'd like the Parmesan grated, if you don't mind."

"Truly, one woof is worth a thousand words."

"No, dear, the martini is when you come back!"

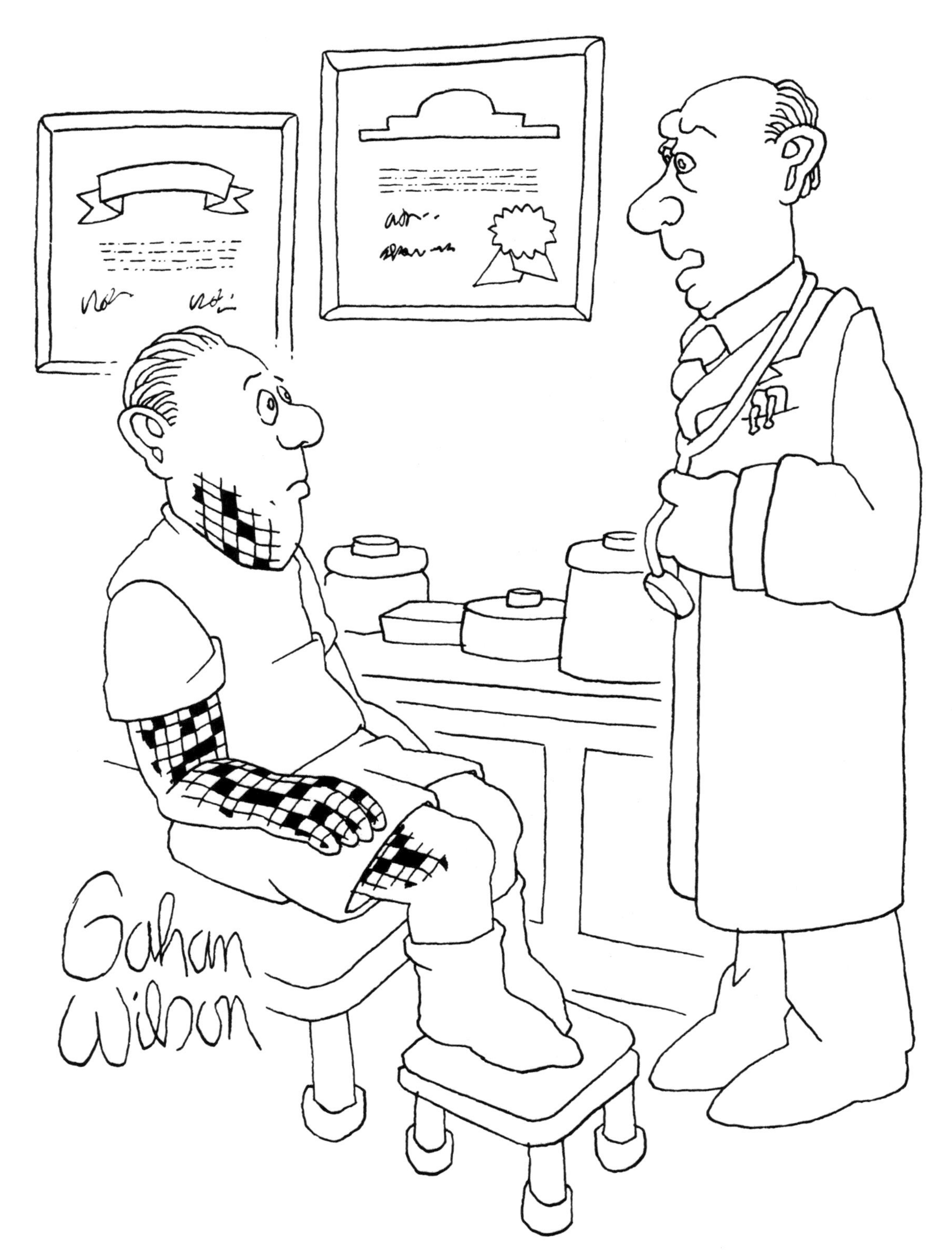

"Very few people are aware that the *New York Times* Sunday crossword puzzle is contagious."

"See how it works? With my book the *reader* pops up!"

"I think it's high time we did something about those things!"

“I *thought* so—they’re trading the bread crumbs for crack cocaine!”

"It's a book."

"Is this your first airplane crash?"

"Hello, I'm Ronnie, your waiter for tonight, and this is Phillip, your water for tonight, and Monty and Ernest and William and Arthur, your rolls for tonight!"

"I liked you better as George Washington."

"And who foots the bill for every one of them? Us *taxpayers*, that's who!"

“I’m sorry, Mr. Humphries, but I’m afraid your car’s flat-lined.”

"Bug off!"

"We think it sort of brightens up the breakfast."

"Sometimes I wish they'd never perfected setless television."

"Don't worry, Phil—I'm going to leave a little peephole so you can watch your weekend football!"

"I do hope you'll excuse the formality of the clamps."

"It's a damn shame we can't get away with this more than one night a year!"

"I think we're losing 'em."

"Hey, baby—that doesn't mean *you!*"

"I guess stepping out on the balcony wasn't such a hot idea!"

"*That* was the scene that's supposed to scare everyone to death?"

"I don't suppose it ever crosses their minds how hard it is to clean up after them!"

"Nobody's spotted us so far!"

"How about resolving that, starting next year, you won't be such a total jerk?"

"Whatever else, it's been something wonderful for the crops!"

"I'm sorry—did I startle you?"

"First time I've ever seen an ATM shred a cardholder!"

"No fair both of us having multiple personalities!"

"They make wonderful boutonnieres!"

"Does the co-op board have any idea when the elevators will be replaced?"

"Here, Spot!"

"I can't believe nobody thought to downsize the office furniture!"

“When the moon hits your eye, like a big pizza pie, that’s amore!”

"Edwin is a great admirer of the late Howard Hughes."

"Would you *mind?*"

"That's a soft *G* in 'EAOGIE', by the way."

"Excuse me for shouting, Harry, but I wanted you to be awake when I slipped in the last brick!"

"Snow men are cute. Mud men are not cute."

"Tell us again how you made up lawyers!"

"I can see it was a serious mistake to have shown you my family album."

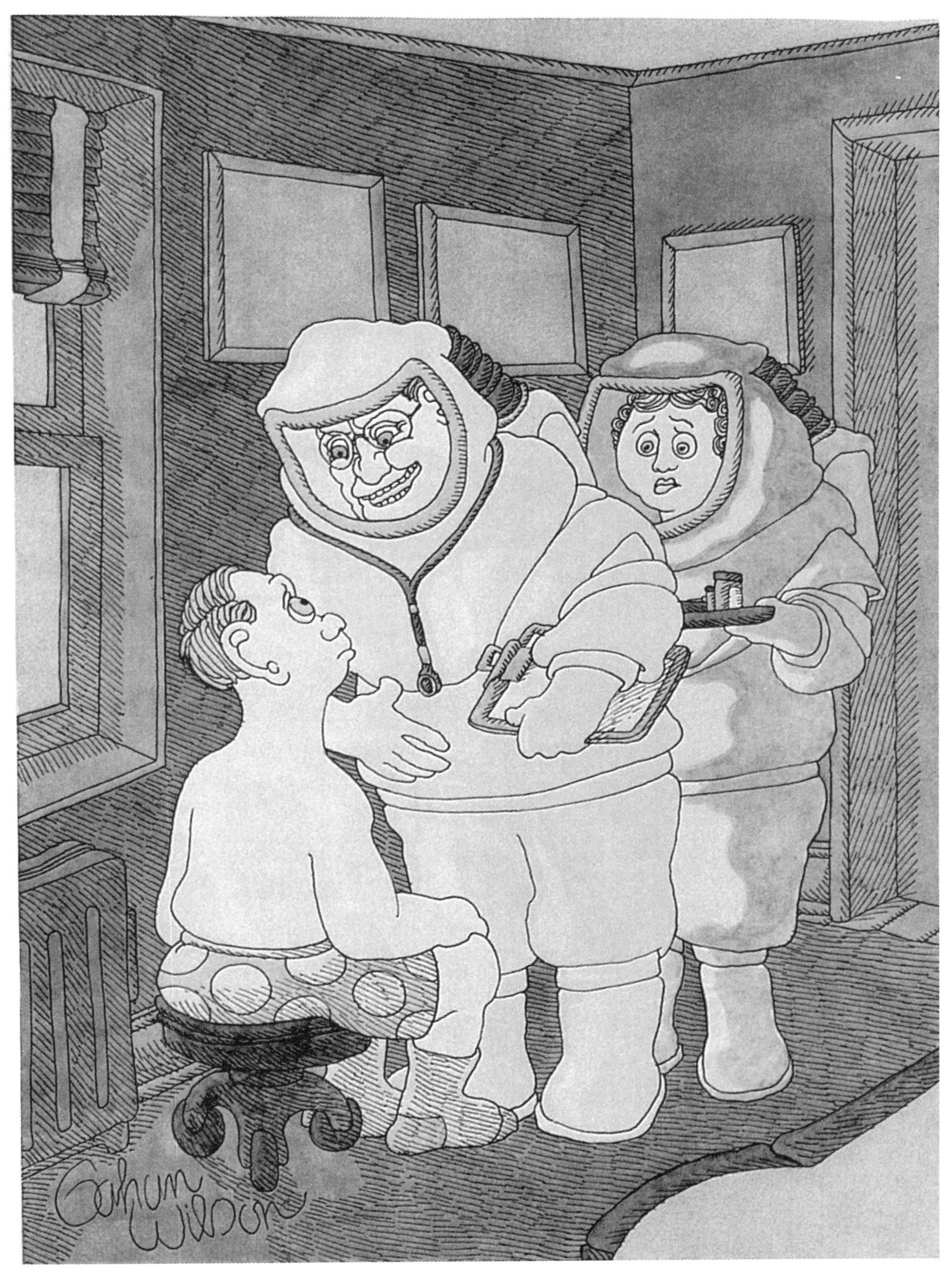

"Please don't be alarmed, Mr. Parker, but those preliminary tests indicate the advisability of a few precautions."

"Sue the bastards."

"Do you suppose all this has anything to do with our eating those genetically-altered tomatoes?"

"Don't try to tell me you never so much as guessed that I might be running this corporation!"

"OK, now I'll be the Ethics Committee and you'll be me."

"I *knew* I heard caroling last night!"

"How about a little more coffee?"

"It's a little something I'm calling *The Book of Revelations!*"

Gahan Wilson

"The reason why our people call this 'commuting' is lost in the mists of history, my son."

FAR TOO CLOSE

"Here they come!"

“Well, it’s really been one of those days!”

"It's all the violence that does it."

"Looking good!"

"Mr. Baxter will see you now."

“Now watch what happens when I let it snap back!”

OF BRAZIL
BIRDS OF MANHATTAN
Gahan Wilson

"Your honor, the jury finds the defendant grumpy, as charged!"

"I'm getting sick and tired of these power surges!"

"They're offering special premiums if we use their service."

“*Where* is still an option for you.”

"And now, if you wouldn't mind, I'd like to fulfill a little dream that has been growing in me since I first came to work for this corporation."

“Frankly, I’m just as glad he left.”

“So—did any of them taste the strychnine?”

"Now that's what I call a sand trap."

JAN FEB MAR APR MAY JUNE JULY AUG SEPT OCT NOV DEC
Gahan Wilson

“They do say it’s the little people after watching the war news on their tiny TV sets.”

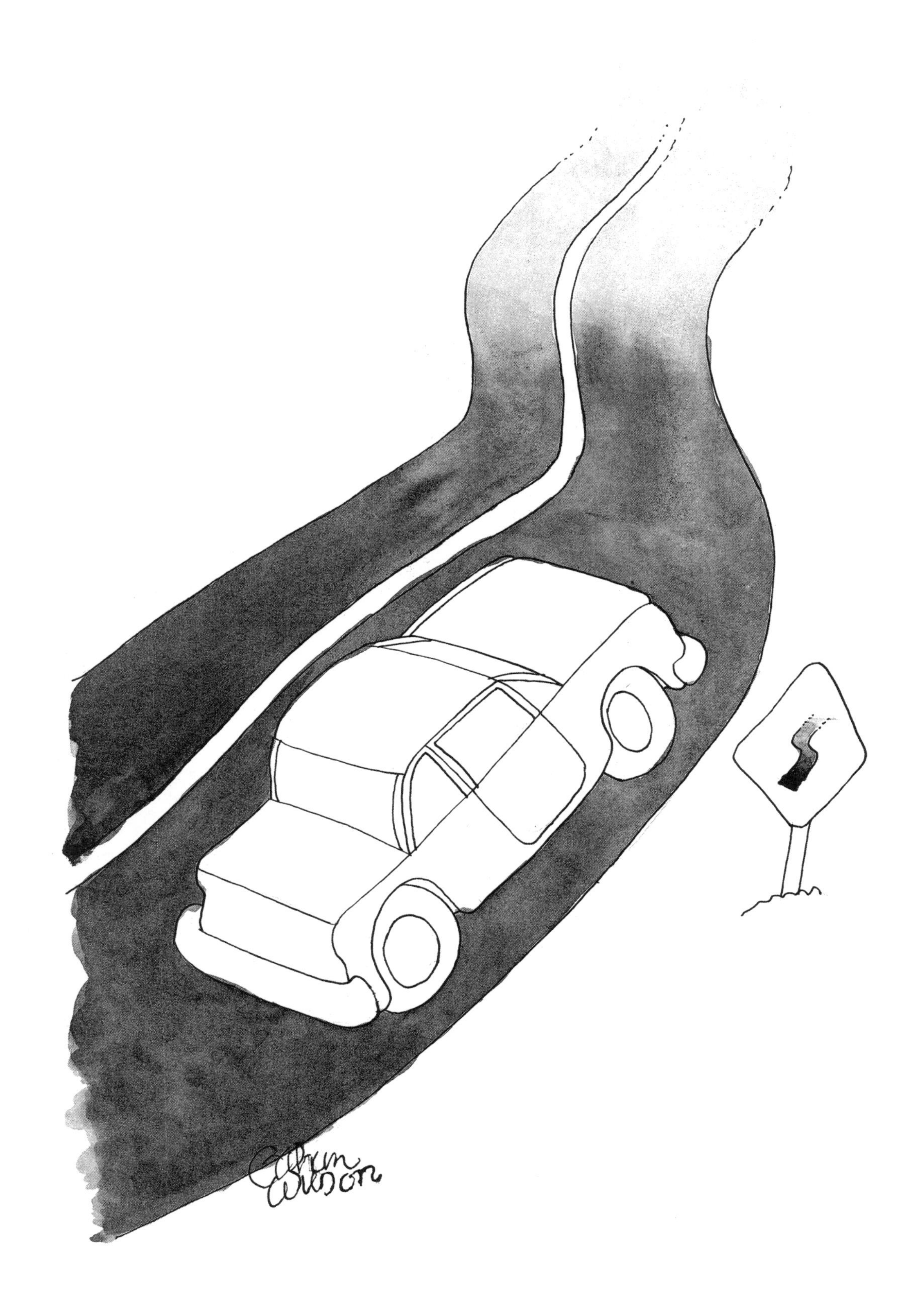

"I'll certainly be glad when you've finishing moulting!"

"I *wondered* where that VCR had got to!"

"Gee, that looks like fun!"

"I thought it was just a phase, but now he's in his forties, I'm not so sure!"

"A promising beginning."

"Have you ever considered surgery?"

"Well, that's it—I've outlived absolutely everybody."

". . . and that's how you kill bison."

“Well, *yes*—the neighbors are something of a problem.”

"Whoops! Sorry, wrong planet."

"You do realize, don't you, that once you bring it home, you can let it out of its little box?"

"Another decade or so, and it'll be warm enough for us."

"John, I wish you'd stop bringing all these horrible diseases back from the city!"

"You're not even slowing me down."

"I don't remember our snowmen being so anatomically correct!"

EBOLA
VIRUS

"If you ask me, wearing these things only makes them nervous."

"Well, sir, it looks like things are getting pretty serious for Peter and Pauline."

"I'm so glad you got rid of that nervous tic!"

"OK, that's fifty dollars for the dog, and five hundred dollars for his list of commands!"

"Of course we made our move out here before the environment went!"

“Look, at least we’re talking.”

"What a nice day!"

"Well, it gives *me* the creeps."

"It's a novelty T-shirt me and the boys designed, Mrs. Patterson!"

"But let's not dwell on the past."

"I've learned one thing in fifty years of scientific research: If it doesn't interest the military-security-industrial complex, it isn't worth shit."

"High time!"

"That's it—you're set for life!"

"I've just joined a support group for boring people."

". . . anyhow, Mrs. Collins and I would sure appreciate it if you fellows would give up!"

"I guess it figures."

"It's wonderful how no one doubts for a moment you ran away and left me!"

HOMELESS
HELP
ME
Gahan Wilson

GEORGE
FISHER
DEC. 16, 1939
APR. 12, 1995
INTERNET: george@ckg.com

"You put family in with the aluminum cans again, Mrs. Price."

"Oh, dear, I was afraid it might turn out to be this kind of spring."

"That was for you."

IF YOU
CAN READ
THIS YOU'RE
TOO CLOSE
Gahan Wilson

"Another sudden thought, dear?"

"None of this seems to be doing me any good at all!"

"Well, I'm certainly glad you finally managed to get that off your chest!"

"Oh, yes, for quite a long time, there, we didn't live in caves!"

"And now I'll take any questions that aren't cranky!"

"The house of Little Red Riding Hood's grandmother is over there, Jack!"

"Don't worry, Mr. and Mrs. Turner, we're doing everything we can to avoid a malpractice suit."

BEWARE THE GRASS
Gahan Wilson

"Well, then, how about this fine Chateauneuf-du-Pape?"

"Next."

"*Now* you're getting the hang of it!"

"It's their idea of cute."

INEPTLY COY
POMPOUSLY INSINCERE
DISGUSTINGLY SENTIMENTAL
Gahan Wilson

“No more peanuts until you buy another round of drinks.”

"If I were you, Brewster, I should very seriously consider an alternative to the career of medicine."

"Way to go, Madge!"

"You *would* find spring depressing!"

"There are far too many balls in your court, Brintner!"

"I was so happy you called, but now I realize I've just been hallucinating!"

"There are no longer seats in tourist, sir."

“Garbage in, garbage out!”

"You know, you may be right about the house tilting."

"It would seem that the apocalypse came as a complete surprise to the citizens of this ordinarily quiet neighborhood in Nutley, New Jersey!"

OUTTA HERE
Gahan Wilson

"So how do you like it on death row?"

"That looks like a popular spot!"

Gahan Wilson

"No one comes close to him for sound bites!"

"I think it's only fair to tell you I've recently been infected with e.coli bacteria!"

"This may be the first case of a near-death experience being witnessed by the patient's attendant physicians."

"Let's go, Elise—I've just discovered this cocktail party is a total fraud!"

"Do you ever catch yourself wondering what the hell's gone wrong with this corporation?"

"There it is—the home of the *National Enquirer*!"

"Isn't that other plane awfully close?"

"Careful—I think we're being filmed!"

WON'T
BEAM
ME
UP
Gahan
Wilson

"They're meat eaters!"

"Excuse me, that's my buzzer."

"Look, I swear to God we're doing everything we can to move the Big Burly Bears' Books!"

“Flight 570 reports its starboard engines sucked in Dasher and Dancer and the port intakes just got Donner and Blitzen!”

SUCKER
SUCKER
SUCKER

"Absolutely not!"

"They say he was abandoned by summer people and raised by squirrels."

"You've been fooling around with alternative medicines, haven't you?"

"So how's everything going?"

LOOK,
I'M USER-
FRIENDLY,
BUT YOU'RE
REALLY
PUSHING IT.
Gahan Wilson

“Remember when the master had a drop of this Armagnac back in ’41 and got into all that trouble with the cops?”

Gahan Wilson

"I'm so glad they both ordered cappuccino!"

"One question: What is your portrait doing on this hundred dollar bill?"

"You know very well we don't abduct anybody without full medical coverage!"

“Yes sir, the place wouldn’t be the same without old Bosley here!”

"Well, it certainly explains why everyone's so nice!"

"We've never regretted relocating to California!"

"I don't see any sign of him!"

"It's obvious something's gone horribly wrong!"

"But that one there is shaped exactly like a cloud!"

"Don't panic, kid—we're just checking to make sure you're taking good care of your hamster."

"Hi! I'm the Ghost of April Fool's Day Past!"

"Look, you're just as cute as you can be—honestly—but what I really need is a waiter!"

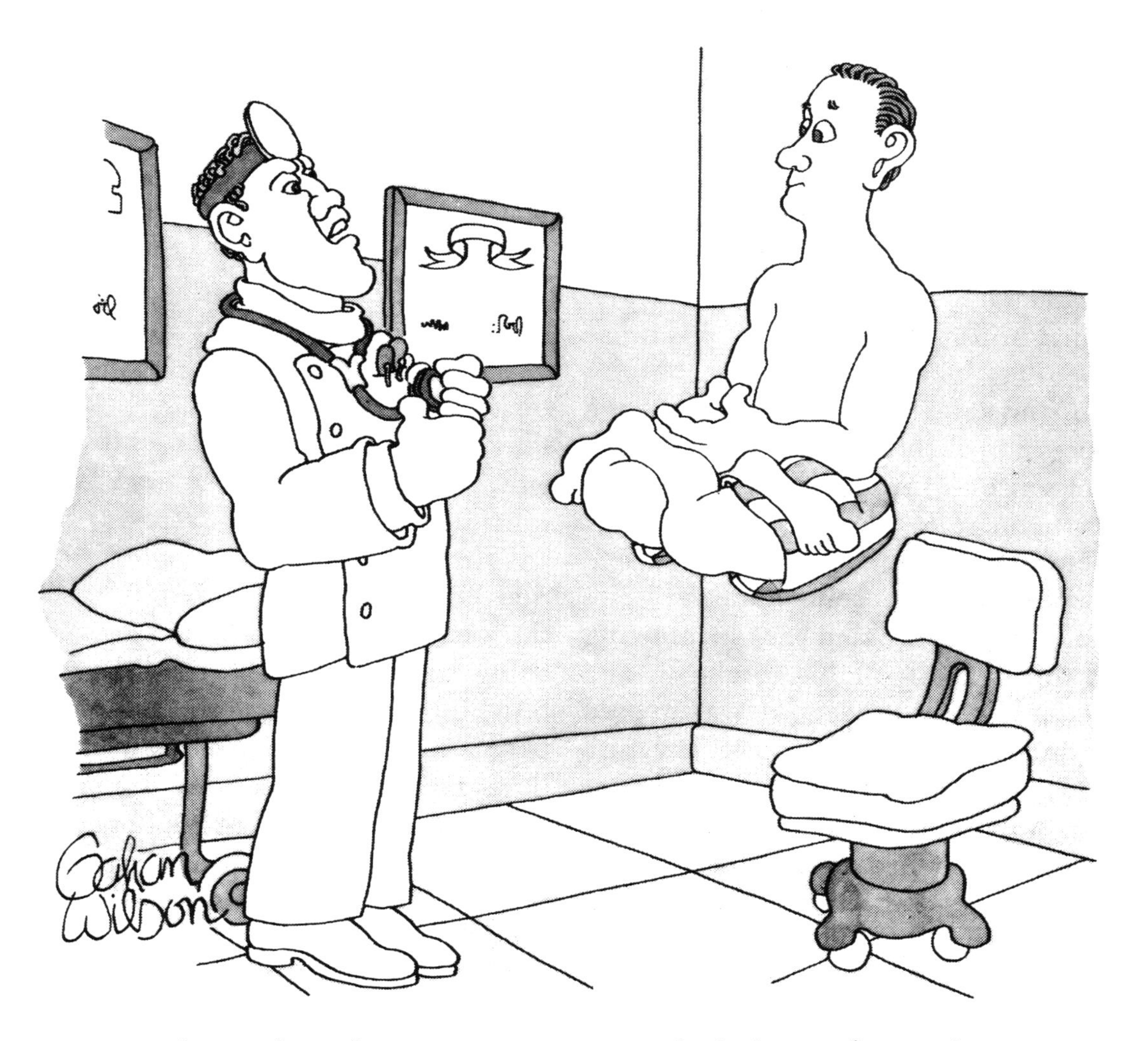

"You have achieved nirvana, Mr. Harper, and a bad case of tennis knee."

"*Got* to have a pair of those!"

"And someday, when you're a little further up the corporate ladder, maybe we'll let you meet J.R. himself!"

"I think it's time I told you my little secret!"

"Sometimes I think perhaps we shouldn't have wiped out the entire family."

"... in other words ..."

"Believe me, Mr. Roberts, checking the wear on a job applicant's molars is just basic company routine."

"I told you he wanted a tiny, little door all his own."

“Those little bowls have saved us no end of trouble!”

"I'm afraid you may have bought the child one too many Barbies!"

"First time I've ever seen the little guys fight back!"

"Oh, boy—a whole platterful of cheap, packaged meat extender."

HUMOR
Gahan Wilson

"Just when did you acquire those tattoos, Warner?"

"But first I must inject you with some harmless preservatives and food dyes!"

"I've had just about as much of this as I'm going to take!"

"It's a good thing intolerable crowding is an integral part of our system!"

"Let's get the hell out of here!"

"Your usual one too many, sir."

"For God's sake, Parker, show some guts and stand up to them!"

"Here comes someone new, everybody!"

"That was very thoughtless of you!"

"Just *love* your campy lawn ornaments!"

". . . whereas this machine translates female speech into male speech!"

"So then Mr. Brewster, who was a cost analyst for an advertising agency, drove his car all the way from Westport, Connecticut, to New York City!"

“Oh, darn!”

"You wear too many clothes."

"We're no longer standing in the wind, Roger."

"Don't you *dare* scratch that couch!"

"I guess it's probably a perfectly logical development."

"Yes, general, I can see as how they would make you, in particular, feel insignificant."

Gahan Wilson

"I guess we better break up the party."

"NO."

"Not you, too!"

"Innovative stuff!"

"But, in the end, you will become bored with that, too."

“Congratulations, sir—your child has blossomed!”

MARTY'S BAR
MARTY'S
SUICIDAL
DEPRESSION
HOUR 3-4
Gahan Wilson

"Believe me—if you could see yourself, you'd drop the whole idea!"

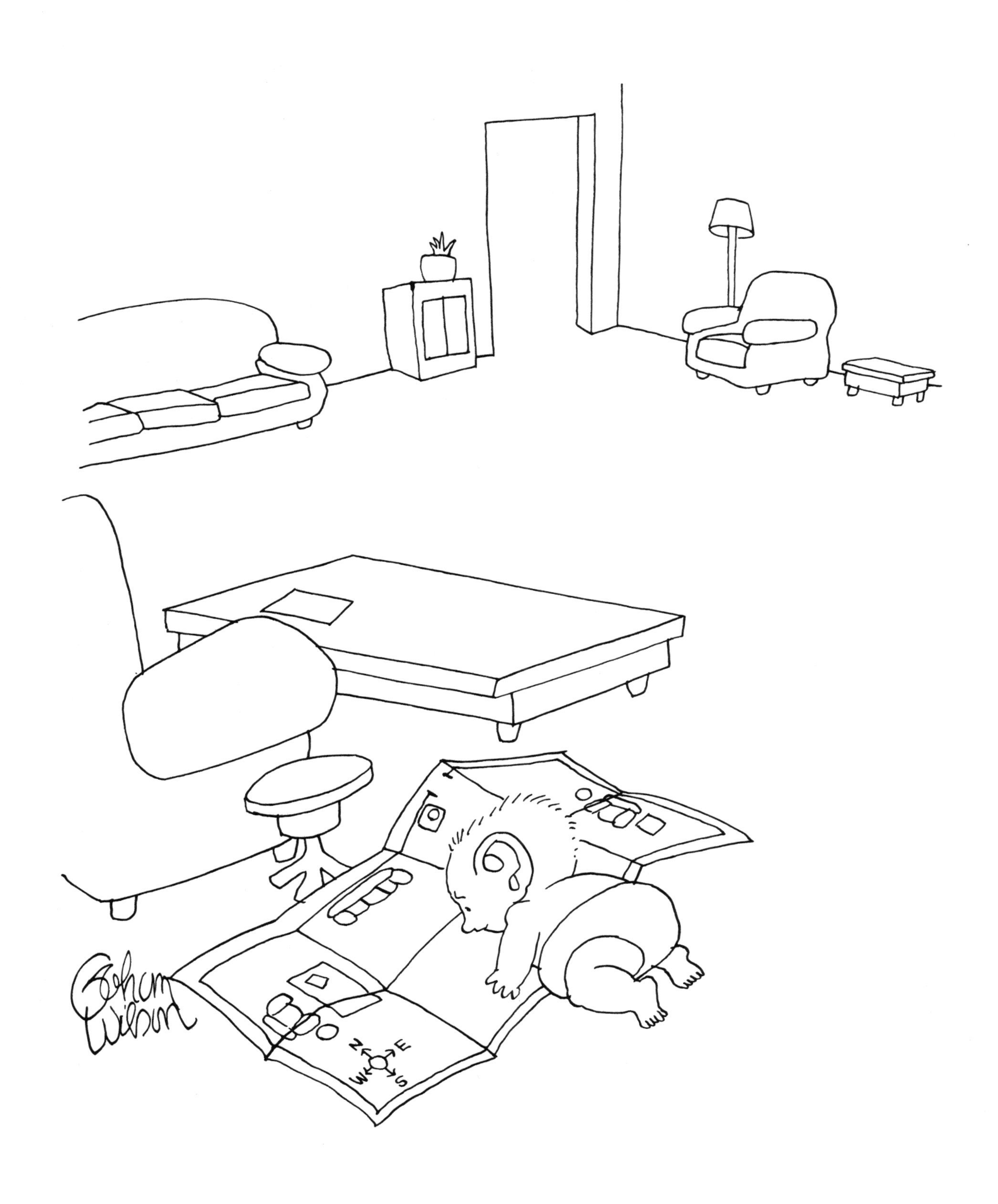
Gahan Wilson
N
E
W
S

“I guess it’s clipping time again.”

"Nobody told me about THIS!"

"Gordon, I wish you'd stop wearing that creepy camouflage!"

"They're Secret Service. They appeared the day Billy decided he wanted to be President when he grew up."

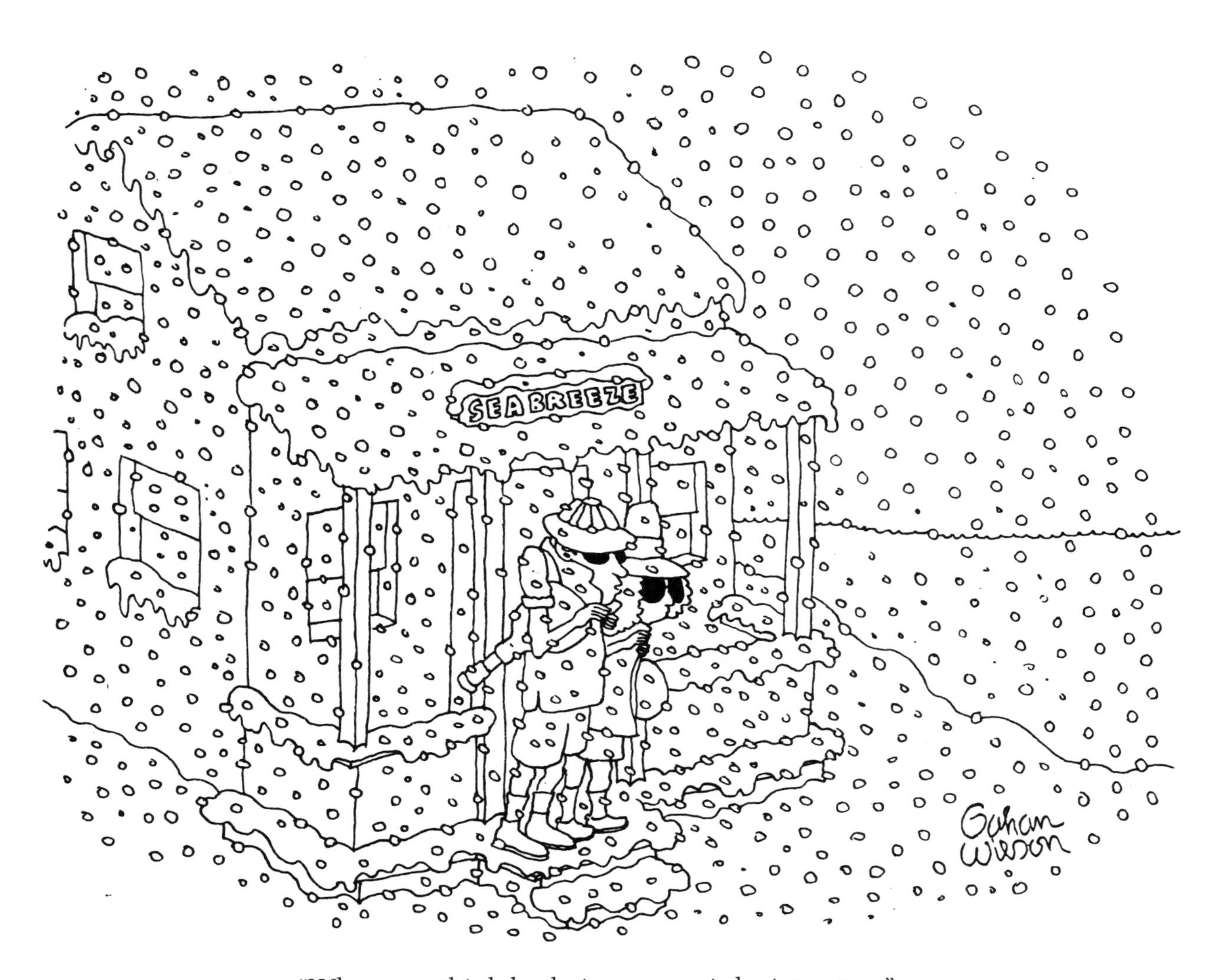

"When you think back, it was a weird winter, too."

DRIVER HATES YOU
Gahan Wilson

"I'll take it."

"Let's get the hell out of here!"

"I hate it when he plays through!"

INTERACTIVE TV

"Sure makes a change from New York!"

"They've left."

GAHAN WILSON

Gahan Wilson's cartoons have appeared in *Playboy, The New Yorker, Weird Tales, Gourmet, Punch, Paris Match*, and *The National Lampoon*. Fifteen individual collections of his work have been published, including *Is Nothing Sacred?, Playboy's Gahan Wilson, Gahan Wilson's America, The Man in the Cannibal Pot*, and *and then we'll get him! Still Weird*, Wilson's first major collection, included both new material and cartoons selected from earlier collections. *Even Weirder*, a follow-up to *Still Weird*, includes never-before-published cartoons seen here for the first time.

Wilson has also written and illustrated a number of children's books, including a picture book, *The Bang Bang Family*, and a series of adventures for *Harry the Fat Bear Spy*. For adults, Wilson has written two mystery novels, *Eddy Deco's Last Caper* and *Everybody's Favorite Duck*, and a large number of horror short stories, which have appeared in *Playboy, Omni, The Magazine of Fantasy & Science Fiction,* and numerous anthologies.

Recent projects include graphic novels adapting the works of Ambrose Bierce and Edgar Allan Poe, a set of trading cards featuring Wilson's demonic baseball players, and his first animated work, a cartoon short, "Gahan Wilson's Diner," released by 20th Century–Fox.

Wilson has also worked on a feature film for Steven Spielberg's Amblin Entertainment, a TV special for Disney, and an animated sitcom for Universal Pictures. He is presently working on a cartoon special for Nickelodeon.